James wakes up.
He makes a plan.
It will be a good day.

James will sail his tug.
He will sail his tug in the tub.

James makes a lake in the tub.
He waits for a big lake.

But James can not wait.
He takes out his games.
He plays on the rug.

The lake James made is big.
The tug sails and sails.
It makes its way out of the tub.

James plays and plays.
The tug sails down.
It sails on the rug.

Mom wakes up.
Her face is red and mad.
She has lots to say.

James has to mop the wet mess.
He gets a pail.
It is not a good day!